CW00349307

# The
# ROYAL HORTICULTURAL SOCIETY
## Book of Days

# The
# Language of Flowers

FRANCES LINCOLN

Frances Lincoln Limited
4 Torriano Mews
Torriano Avenue
London NW5 2RZ

The Royal Horticultural Society Book of Days
Copyright © Frances Lincoln Limited 1996
Illustrations copyright © The Royal Horticultural Society 1995

Design by David Fordham

All rights reserved.
No part of this publication may be reproduced, stored in a retrieval system or transmitted, in any
form, or by any means, electronic, mechanical, photocopying, recording or otherwise, without
either the prior permission in writing from the publishers or a licence permitting restricted
copying. In the United Kingdom such licences are issued by the Copyright Licensing Agency,
90 Tottenham Court Road, London W1P 9HE.

British Library cataloguing-in-publication data.
A catalogue record for this book is available from the British Library.

ISBN 0-7112-1115-9

Typeset by SX Composing

Printed in Hong Kong

# The
# Language of Flowers

THE LANGUAGE OF FLOWERS first appeared in recognizable form in 1818, in *Le Langage des fleurs* by 'Charlotte de la Tour' (the pseudonym of Louise Cortambert). This little volume gave 313 messages that could be conveyed by presenting a flower, for the most part messages of love, of supplication, or of the refusal of advances. Some indicated a psychological state ('Patience', 'Voluptuousness', 'Frigidity'), while others gave specific instructions or responses ('My regrets follow you to the grave', 'Better to die than lose one's innocence'). Some meanings were suggested by classical mythology, narcissus indicating 'Egoism', for example; others came from the French vernacular names of the plants (*clandestine*, the French common name of *Leonurus cardiaca*, became 'Secrecy', a meaning that did not make much sense in England, where the common name of the plant was motherwort).

The language of flowers quickly became a popular nineteenth-century amusement – or perhaps 'amusements' would be a better word, for it appeared in different forms in French, German and English, and in each of those languages there were rival versions. By the 1830s, Charlotte de la Tour had been translated and adapted in England. Robert Tyas's *Sentiment of Flowers* (1853) and *Language of Flowers* (1869) became the best known adaptations. Like other English authors, Tyas applied traditional associations in favour of Charlotte de la Tour's when the French system conflicted with Shakespeare (thanks to Ophelia, rosemary stood for 'Remembrance', instead of 'Your presence revives me'). Associations with Roman Catholicism were removed, substituted by robust Protestant meanings (passion flowers changed their meaning from 'Faith' to 'Superstition'), and the sexual content of the French original was toned down (tuberoses ceased to mean 'Voluptuousness' and came to signify 'I have seen a lovely girl').

Some authors, most notably the 'poetical basket-weaver' Thomas Miller in his *Poetical Language of Flowers* (1847), drew up rival systems based on English literary allusion, but such attempts did not compete well with the system already established. Nor did a curious work, *The Catholic Language of Flowers* (1861) by 'The young ladies of Gumley House' (a Catholic convent), dedicated to Nicholas Wiseman, the Roman Catholic cardinal. After 1869, however, and the publication of John Ingram's *Flora Symbolica*, a new trend developed for books that were eclectic and comprehensive, giving multiple meanings where these existed.

By the 1850s, the language of flowers was crossing the Atlantic, but American versions had their own distinct character. They added entries for newly introduced exotics, especially greenhouse plants, which were given meanings before they received common names. They also introduced many transatlantic confusions: where English and American plant names differed, American compilers frequently cited the same plant under different names.

The publication of language of flowers books continued in America until the end of the century but declined in England after 1870, although the subject enjoyed a revival in popularity as a theme for picture postcards during the Edwardian era.

Given the possibilities for confusion resulting from the conflicting meanings to be found in different books, it is surprising that the language of flowers does not play a more significant role in nineteenth-century fiction, but its purpose was for amusement and this diary sets out to amuse today's readers with some of the conflicts of meaning that made up this rich and entertaining form of communication.

BRENT ELLIOT
*The Royal Horticultural Society*

# *Rosa indica*

A hand-coloured stipple engraving by

Pierre-Joseph Redouté from his *Les roses* (1817-24)

THE LANGUAGE OF FLOWERS DEVELOPED during the years when Redouté was publishing *Les roses*, and many different species and varieties of rose earned separate entries in the language. The rose on its own was almost universally given the meaning 'Beauty' until 1869, when John Ingram's *Flora Symbolica* identified it with 'Love' instead. Additional meanings included 'Genteel, pretty' and, in *The Catholic Language of Flowers* (1861), 'The sacred heart of Jesus'.

# Crocus vernus

A hand-coloured stipple engraving of spring crocus by

<small>PIERRE-JOSEPH REDOUTÉ</small> from his *Les liliacées* (1802-16)

IN MOST LANGUAGE OF FLOWERS BOOKS, the crocus's association with early spring earned it the meaning of 'Youthfulness' or 'Youthful gladness'. Variants include 'Pleasures of hope', in Robert Tyas's *Language of Flowers* (1869); 'Smiles, cheerfulness', in some anonymous works; and 'Rashness' in *The Catholic Language of Flowers* (1861). In later works, the crocus sometimes borrowed the meaning of the saffron crocus, 'Abuse not'.

1

2

3

4

5

6

7

# January

8

9

10

11

12

13

14

# *Primula auricula*

A hand-coloured stipple engraving of auriculas by

Pierre-Joseph Redouté from his *Choix des plus belles fleurs* (1827-33)

The auricula was originally more popular in England than in France and thus was not included in Charlotte de la Tour's early and influential book, *Langage des fleurs* (1818). All English language of flowers books initially agreed on 'Painting' as the meaning, probably because interest in auriculas centred on their colours and edgings. *The Catholic Language of Flowers* (1861) redefined it as 'True happiness'.

# Magnolia discolor

A hand-coloured stipple engraving by

Pierre-Joseph Redouté from Duhamel du Monceau's *Traité des arbres et arbustes* (1801-25)

THE MAGNOLIA ENTERED THE LANGUAGE OF FLOWERS rather late; it appeared in John Ingram's *Flora Symbolica* (1869) meaning 'Love of nature, magnificence'. Its only previous appearance was in *The Catholic Language of Flowers* (1861), where it symbolized 'Lively faith'.

15

16

17

18

19

20

21

# January

22

23

24

25

26

27

28

A CULTIVAR OF

# *Hyacinthus orientalis*

A hand-coloured stipple engraving by

Pierre-Joseph Redouté from his *Choix des plus belles fleurs* (1827-33)

I N GREEK MYTHOLOGY, Hyacinthus was killed by Apollo during the course of a game. Charlotte de la Tour therefore gave the hyacinth the meaning of '*Jeu*', translated as 'Sport' or 'Games'. Thomas Miller attempted to change its meaning to 'Truth' and 'St Joseph's early life' was proposed by *The Catholic Language of Flowers* (1861), but neither proved popular. Some later publications distinguished between white hyacinths ('Unobtrusive loveliness') and purple ('Sorrowful; I am sorry').

# *Narcissus tazetta*

A hand-coloured stipple engraving of tazetta daffodils by

Pierre-Joseph Redouté from his *Choix des plus belles fleurs* (1827-33)

There is no botanical distinction between a daffodil and a narcissus, and it is not always easy to tell which is meant in language of flowers books. Charlotte de la Tour gave the narcissus the meaning of '*Egoisme*' (in Greek myth, Narcissus fell in love with himself), and was followed by English writers, with such variations as 'Self-esteem' and 'Self-love'.

29

30

31

1

2

3

4

# February

5

6

7

8

9

10

11

# *Camellia* 'Incarnata'

A hand-coloured line engraving by

ALFRED CHANDLER from Chandler and Booth's

*Illustrations and Descriptions of . . . the Natural Order of Camellieae* (1830-31)

CAMELLIAS WERE GENERALLY TREATED as greenhouse plants in the early nineteenth century and only entered the language of flowers in the second quarter of the century, when their hardiness became apparent. Robert Tyas gave camellias the meaning of 'Unpretending excellence', a meaning later confined to red-flowered forms, while white ones came to mean 'Perfected loveliness' and, according to *The Catholic Language of Flowers* (1861). 'Chastity'.

# *Rosa gallica* 'Maheka'

A hand-coloured stipple engraving by

PIERRE-JOSEPH REDOUTÉ from his *Les roses* (1817-24)

THE NUMBER OF MEANINGS assigned to different types of roses increased in later works on the language of flowers. John Ingram, in his *Flora Symbolica* (1869), gave 'Bashful shame' as the meaning of a deep red rose. *The Catholic Language of Flowers* (1861), attempting to lift its readers' minds to higher things, suggested 'England' as an alternative meaning.

12

13

14

15

16

17

18

# February

19

20

21

22

23

24

25

# Hedera helix

A hand-coloured engraving of ivy from the second edition of

WILLIAM CURTIS'S *Flora Londinensis* (1835)

'FRIENDSHIP' AND 'FIDELITY' were the most frequent meanings given for ivy. 'Marriage' was an additional meaning, and some later books specified that a sprig of ivy with tendrils meant 'Assiduous to please'.

# *Camellia* 'Corallina'

A hand-coloured line engraving by

Alfred Chandler of the camellia he raised in 1819, from Chandler and Booth's

*Illustrations and Descriptions of . . . the Natural Order of Camellieae* (1830-31)

ALTHOUGH VARIETIES OF YELLOW AND RED CAMELLIA were developed during the early decades of the nineteenth century, it was only in the second half of the century that the colour of camellias made a difference to their meaning in the language of flowers. The red camellia retained the original meaning for the genus, 'Unpretending excellence'. 'Beauty is your only attraction' is given in some later books as a meaning for *Camellia japonica*.

26

27

28

29

1

2

3

# *March*

4

5

6

7

8

9

10

# Rosa pimpinellifolia inermis

A hand-coloured stipple engraving of the thornless rose by

Pierre-Joseph Redouté from his *Les roses* (1817-24)

Roses furnished the language of flowers with more nuances of meaning than any other plant. Even a flowerless sprig of rose was used to denote 'Separation' (Thomas Miller), and some later language of flowers books, following John Ingram's *Flora Symbolica* (1869), gave the thornless rose illustrated here as a symbol of 'Early attachment'.

MANY ENGLISH WRITERS gave different entries for daffodil and narcissus. In his *Sentiment of Flowers* (1853), Robert Tyas gave the daffodil the meaning of 'Delusive hope', because 'the flowers of this plant very often fail'. In this he was followed by other later writers, with 'Unrequited love' sometimes appearing as well. In his *Language of Flowers* (1869), Tyas added 'Disdain' as a further meaning. *The Catholic Language of Flowers* (1861) used the daffodil as a sign for 'Folly'.

11

12

13

14

15

16

17

# March

18

19

20

21

22

23

24

A CULTIVAR OF

# *Malus sylvestris*

A hand-coloured stipple engraving of the blossom of a hybrid apple by

PIERRE-JOSEPH REDOUTÉ from Duhamel du Monceau's *Traité des arbres et arbustes* (1801-25)

CHARLOTTE DE LA TOUR GAVE 'PREFERENCE' as the meaning of apple blossom, with the explanation that apple blossom might be preferred to roses. 'Preference' may be found in many English publications, but it was never a favourite meaning. The popular identification of the apple as the biblical fruit of the tree of the knowledge of good and evil led to 'Temptation' becoming more widely adopted. An additional meaning, 'Fame speaks him great and good', was also widespread.

# *Rosa sulfurea*

A hand-coloured stipple engraving of a yellow rose by

<small>PIERRE-JOSEPH REDOUTÉ</small> from his *Les roses* (1817-24)

F<small>ROM</small> C<small>HARLOTTE DE LA</small> T<small>OUR ONWARDS</small>, almost all language of flowers books gave the meaning of a yellow rose as 'Infidelity'. Variants from the later, more eclectic works included 'Jealousy' and 'Decrease of Love'; in some American publications these definitions apply only to the yellow sweetbriar.

25

26

27

28

29

30

31

# April

1

2

3

4

5

6

7

# *Lilium candidum*

A hand-coloured stipple engraving of a Madonna lily by

Pierre-Joseph Redouté from his *Les liliacées* (1802-16)

Charlotte de la Tour gave the meaning of the white lily as 'Majesty', drawing on the French poet Boisjolin who wrote that the lily was the king of flowers, as the rose was the queen. 'Purity and modesty' were the preferred meanings in England. When other white lilies were introduced into cultivation, this lily took the name Madonna lily and was associated with 'Mary immaculate' in *The Catholic Language of Flowers* (1861).

CULTIVARS OF

# Tulipa gesneriana

A hand-coloured stipple engraving by

Pierre-Joseph Redouté from his *Choix des plus belles fleurs* (1827-33)

Charlotte de la Tour and her English successors all agreed that the tulip should represent 'Declaration of love'. *The Catholic Language of Flowers* (1861) changed this to 'Presumption'. Later books gave 'Fame', originally the meaning of tulip tree, and 'Charity', originally the meaning of turnip, both perhaps originating as typographical errors. 'Beautiful eyes' was attributed to the variegated tulip and 'Hopeless love' to the yellow tulip while 'Declaration of love' was eventually restricted to the red tulip.

8

9

10

11

12

13

14

# April

15

16

17

18

19

20

21

# *Fritillaria imperialis*

A hand-coloured stipple engraving of a crown imperial by

Pierre-Joseph Redouté from his *Choix des plus belles fleurs* (1827-33)

A S ITS NAME IMPLIES, the crown imperial had been associated with imperial power since the sixteenth century, and books on the language of flowers vacillated between 'Power' and 'Majesty' as its meaning. The only minor deviation from this is found in *The Catholic Language of Flowers* (1861), where its meaning was given as 'Sovereignty'.

# *Iris* 'Monspur'

A water-colour drawing by

Miss Williamson, made in 1905 for Ellen Willmott from a specimen in her garden at Warley Place

CHARLOTTE DE LA TOUR GAVE THE MEANING OF THE IRIS as 'Message', drawing an analogy between the many colours of iris varieties and the rainbow which was God's message to mankind. De la Tour's meaning was universally followed. Even *The Catholic Language of Flowers* (1861) went no further than to specify its meaning as 'Messages from heaven'.

22

23

24

25

26

27

28

# April/May

29

30

1

2

3

4

5

# Convallaria majalis

A hand-coloured stipple engraving of lily of the valley by

PIERRE-JOSEPH REDOUTÉ from his *Les liliacées* (1802-16)

VIRTUALLY EVERY LANGUAGE OF FLOWERS BOOK gave 'Return of happiness' as the meaning for the lily of the valley. The only exception, as so often, was *The Catholic Language of Flowers* (1861), which redefined it as 'Reserve'. In some later books the additional meaning 'Unconscious sweetness' was given.

# Wisteria sinensis

A chromolithograph of the drawing by

A. J. WENDEL from Hendrik Witte's *Flora* (1868)

THE WISTERIA WAS A LATE ADDITION to the language of flowers books, first appearing in the 1860s when it became popular as an open-air climber (having previously been treated as a greenhouse plant). The later books gave its meaning as 'Welcome, fair stranger'.

6

7

8

9

10

11

12

# *May*

13

14

15

16

17

18

19

# A Noisette rose

A hand-coloured stipple engraving by

PIERRE-JOSEPH REDOUTÉ from his *Les roses* (1817-24)

CHARLOTTE DE LA TOUR CHOSE ROSEBUDS to signify a young girl, and in this she was followed by the English writers. In the second half of the nineteenth century, some books distinguished between white rosebuds ('Girlhood'), red rosebuds ('Pure and lovely') and moss rosebuds ('Confession of love'), this latter meaning derived from Thomas Miller's *Poetical Language of Flowers* (1847).

# Polygonatum multiflorum

A hand-coloured stipple engraving of Solomon's seal by

Pierre-Joseph Redouté from his *Les liliacées* (1802-16)

CALLED 'OUR LADY'S SEAL' IN MEDIEVAL TIMES, polygonatum was renamed after the Protestant Reformation, in order to avoid associations with the Virgin Mary, and became known as Solomon's seal. Possibly because of its continuing, if transformed, religious associations, the language of flowers overlooked this plant. For the same reason, however, *The Catholic Language of Flowers* (1861) found a place for it, representing 'Wisdom'.

20

21

22

23

24

25

26

27

28

29

30

31

1

2

# Lathyrus odoratus

A hand-coloured stipple engraving of sweet peas by

Pierre-Joseph Redouté from his *Choix des plus belles fleurs* (1827-33)

THE SWEET PEA WAS INTRODUCED into cultivation in Europe in the early eighteenth century. The flower's popularity grew during the nineteenth century, but it only became fashionable in the Edwardian period. Thomas Miller's *Poetical Language of Flowers* (1847) was the first book to list an interpretation of the sweet pea: here it stood simply for 'Pleasure'. From the 1840s most books expanded on Miller, giving 'Delicate pleasure' and 'Departure' as alternative meanings.

# *Rosa damascena*

A hand-coloured stipple engraving of a Damask rose by

Pierre-Joseph Redouté from his *Les roses* (1817-24)

CHARLOTTE DE LA TOUR and her English follower Robert Tyas gave the meaning of the Damask rose as 'Beauty ever new'. This seems not to have been specific enough for the needs of English writers, for it is more common to find 'Freshness of complexion' or, later, 'Brilliant complexion' given instead. *The Catholic Language of Flowers* (1861) redefined it as 'Beneficence'.

3

4

5

6

7

8

9

# June

10

11

12

13

14

15

16

# *Papaver somniferum*

A hand-coloured stipple engraving of poppies by

<small>PIERRE-JOSEPH REDOUTÉ</small> from his *Choix des plus belles fleurs* (1827-33)

CHARLOTTE DE LA TOUR GAVE THE MEANING of the white poppy as 'Sleep of the heart' and the red poppy 'Consolation' (a meaning shared with the snowdrop). English writers wrestled with the contradiction between this and the traditional association of poppies with sleep. As a result, poppies came to mean both 'Oblivion' and 'Consolation to the sick'; and some works listed 'Fantastic extravagance' as an extra meaning for the scarlet poppy.

# Paeonia lactiflora

A hand-coloured stipple engraving by

Pierre-Joseph Redouté from his *Choix des plus belles fleurs* (1827-33)

THE SEVENTEENTH-CENTURY POET René Rapin had characterized the peony as the flower of shame:
Whose Blushes might the Praise of Virture claim,
But her vile Scent betrays they rise from shame . . .
For this reason Charlotte de la Tour and her English followers gave the meaning of the peony as 'Shame', although some later publications altered this to 'Bashfulness'.

17

18

19

20

21

22

23

# June

## 24

## 25

## 26

## 27

## 28

## 29

## 30

# Syringa vulgaris

A hand-coloured stipple engraving of lilac by

PIERRE-JOSEPH REDOUTÉ from his *Choix des plus belles fleurs* (1827-33)

BECAUSE IT FLOWERED EARLY IN THE SEASON, Charlotte de la Tour chose the lilac to signify 'First emotions of love', and was followed in this by most English writers. A few works gave 'Forsaken', which was more usually the meaning ascribed to the anemone. *The Catholic Language of Flowers* (1861) redefined lilac as meaning 'Meekness'.

A VARIETY OF

# *Rosa gallica*

A hand-coloured stipple engraving by

PIERRE-JOSEPH REDOUTÉ from his *Les roses* (1817-24)

ROSES HAD MANY SUBTLETIES OF MEANING in the language of flowers. As early as 1818, Charlotte de la Tour gave distinct meanings for a rose leaf ('I never importune') and a rose presented in a tuft of grass ('There is everything to be gained by good company'). In some later books, a full-blown rose placed over two buds in a bouquet was used to indicate 'Secrecy'.

*July*

1

2

3

4

5

6

7

# July

8

9

10

11

12

13

14

# *Aesculus hippocastanum*

A hand-coloured stipple engraving of horse chestnut by

Pierre-Joseph Redouté from Duhamel du Monceau's *Traité des arbres et arbustes* (1801-25)

WHEN THE LANGUAGE OF FLOWERS WAS DEVELOPING, the horse chestnut was a rich man's tree, charac-terized by Charlotte de la Tour as astonishing the vulgar with its useless luxury – useless because its fruits were inedible. 'Luxury' therefore remained its meaning, except in *The Catholic Language of Flowers* (1861) where it was used to mean 'Fraternal affection'.

# *Antirrhinum majus*

A hand-coloured stipple engraving of a snapdragon by

P<small>IERRE</small>-J<small>OSEPH</small> R<small>EDOUTÉ</small> from his *Choix des plus belles fleurs* (1827-33)

C<small>HARLOTTE DE LA</small> T<small>OUR AND THE EARLIER</small> E<small>NGLISH WRITERS</small> on the language of flowers gave the meaning of the snapdragon as 'Presumption'. In his *Poetical Language of Flowers* (1847), Thomas Miller concocted the alternative meaning of 'Refusal' and this appears in some later works, one American book abridging its meaning simply to 'No'.

15

16

17

18

19

20

21

# July

22

23

24

25

26

27

28

# Lonicera caprifolium

A hand-coloured stipple engraving of honeysuckle by

Pierre-Joseph Redouté from his *Choix des plus belles fleurs* (1827-33)

'BONDS OF LOVE' was given as the meaning of the honeysuckle by Charlotte de la Tour and most of her English successors. Thomas Miller's *Poetical Language of Flowers* (1847) attempted to replace this by 'Devoted affection' and this meaning was picked up by some of the later works. 'Sweetness of disposition' was an additional meaning which appeared in most English works, later augmented in American publications as 'Generous and devoted affection'.

A FORM OF

# *Robinia hispida*

A hand-coloured stipple engraving of rose acacia by

Pierre-Joseph Redouté from Duhamel du Monceau's *Traité des arbres et arbustes* (1801-25)

CHARLOTTE DE LA TOUR USED THE ROSE ACACIA (*Robinia hispida*) to mean 'Elegance' and the common 'acacia' (*Robinia pseudoacacia*) to mean 'Platonic love'. This latter meaning was rephrased by most of her English followers as 'Chaste love' or, later, 'Friendship'.

29

30

31

1

2

3

4

# *August*

5

6

7

8

9

10

11

# Ipomoea quamoclit

A hand-coloured stipple engraving of a morning glory by

Pierre-Joseph Redouté from his *Choix des plus belles fleurs* (1827-33)

Predictably for a clinging plant, the ipomoea was used by Charlotte de la Tour and her English followers to mean 'I attach myself to you'. This was later to become merely 'Attachment' and was sometimes reserved for red-flowered species, while others were given the meaning 'Affectation'.

# *Passiflora caerulea*

A hand-coloured stipple engraving of a passion flower by

Mary Lawrance from her *A Collection of Passion Flowers coloured from Nature* (1799-1802)

The passion flower had been so called since the sixteenth century because its unusual floral structure gave rise to analogies with the passion of Christ. French books on the language of flowers therefore gave its meaning as 'Faith'; Protestant English authors, however, were suspicious of this meaning and usually substituted 'Superstition'.

12

13

14

15

16

17

18

# August

19

20

21

22

23

24

25

# *Iris × monnieri*

A water-colour drawing by

Miss Williamson, made in 1905 for Ellen Willmott from a specimen in her garden at Warley Place

FLAMME OR *FLAMBE* WAS A FRENCH VERNACULAR NAME for the yellow iris; Charlotte de la Tour, in making 'Flame' its meaning in the language of flowers, was simply adopting a common convention. English writers tried to find interpretations that would justify the meaning, and so 'Ardour' and 'Flame of Love' will often be found in English language of flowers books.

# Clematis viticella

A hand-coloured stipple engraving by

PIERRE-JOSEPH REDOUTÉ from Duhamel du Monceau's *Traité des arbres et arbustes* (1801-25)

CLEMATIS HAD TWO CONTRASTING MEANINGS in the language of flowers. The earlier meaning, given by Charlotte de la Tour, was 'artifice', derived from beggars' use of clematis leaves to produce skin ulcers so as to excite pity. The young George Eliot was nicknamed 'Clematis' because of the plant's alternative meaning, 'Mental beauty'.

26

27

28

29

30

31

1

# September

2

3

4

5

6

7

8

# Tropaeolum majus

A hand-coloured stipple engraving of a nasturtium by

Pierre-Joseph Redouté from his *Choix des plus belles fleurs* (1827-33)

English plant breeders in the early nineteenth century frequently gave their flowers military names: auriculas, polyanthus and pinks bore titles like 'Defiance', 'Britannia' and 'Hertfordshire Hero'. In his *Sentiment of Flowers* (1853), Robert Tyas gave 'Patriotism' as the nasturtium's meaning. *The Catholic Language of Flowers* (1861), perhaps responding to this definition, redefined it as 'The applause of the world'.

Charlotte de la Tour and most of her English followers gave the meaning of the white rose as 'Silence', from its association with the classical god of silence. Some later works changed this to 'I am worthy of you', while specifying that a withered white rose meant 'Transient impressions', and a dried one, 'Death is preferable to loss of innocence'.

9

10

11

12

13

14

15

# September

**16**

---

**17**

---

**18**

---

**19**

---

**20**

---

**21**

---

**22**

---

# Nerium oleander

A hand-coloured stipple engraving of oleander by

Pierre-Joseph Redouté from his *Choix des plus belles fleurs* (1827-33)

O LEANDER HAS A LONG HISTORY IN EUROPE, being known in the Mediterranean from classical times and grown in England from the sixteenth century. Nevertheless, it entered the language of flowers late, and is not to be found until the middle of the nineteenth century, when its meaning is given as 'Beware', possibly because, although used medicinally in mild doses, most of its parts are poisonous.

# Lilium bulbiferum

A hand-coloured stipple engraving by

PIERRE-JOSEPH REDOUTÉ from his *Les liliacées* (1802-16)

L ILIES OF COLOURS OTHER THAN WHITE were late additions to the language of flowers. In 1861, *The Catholic Language of Flowers* gave 'A passionate disposition' as the meaning for orange lilies, while later American books identified yellow lilies with 'Falsehood, gaiety'.

23

24

25

26

27

28

29

# September/October

30

1

2

3

4

5

6

# *Jasminum grandiflorum*

A hand-coloured stipple engraving of Spanish jasmine by

Pierre-Joseph Redouté from his *Choix des plus belles fleurs* (1827-33)

THE COMMON JASMINE, *Jasminum officinale*, was used by Charlotte de la Tour and her English followers to stand for 'Amiableness' or 'Amiability'. The Spanish jasmine shown here, although well known in gardens in de la Tour's time, did not enter the language of flowers until the second half of the nineteenth century, when it came to stand for 'Sensuality'.

# Asphodelus lutea

A hand-coloured stipple engraving of asphodel by

PIERRE-JOSEPH REDOUTÉ from his *Les liliacées* (1802-16)

ASPHODEL WAS A PLANT WITH STRONG CLASSICAL ASSOCIATIONS known to have been used as a funeral decoration, and it was universally adopted to mean 'My regrets follow you to the grave'. Thomas Miller, in his *Poetical Language of Flowers* (1847), altered this slightly to 'Regret and sorrow for the dead'.

7

8

9

10

11

12

13

# October

14

15

16

17

18

19

20

# *Rosa muscosa*

A hand-coloured stipple engraving of the moss rose by

Pierre-Joseph Redouté from his *Les roses* (1817-24)

CHARLOTTE DE LA TOUR GAVE 'LOVE, VOLUPTUOUSNESS' as the meanings of the moss rose, but many English books chastened its meaning to 'Pleasure without alloy', and *The Catholic Language of Flowers* (1861) used it to mean 'Holiness'. A moss rosebud, following Thomas Miller, was used to mean 'Confession of love'.

# Dendranthema indicum

A hand-coloured stipple engraving of chrysanthemum by

PIERRE-JOSEPH REDOUTÉ from his *Choix des plus belles fleurs* (1827-33)

IN HIS *SENTIMENT OF FLOWERS* (1853), Robert Tyas offered 'Cheerfulness in adversity' as the meaning of the chrysanthemum, because it extended the flowering season into the autumn, a formerly bleak time in the flower garden. A similar association with autumn led *The Catholic Language of Flowers* (1861) to redefine it as 'Farewell'. As the varieties of chrysanthemum multiplied, so did their meanings in the language of flowers: red chrysanthemums came to signify 'I love', white to mean 'Truth', and yellow to stand for 'Slighted love'.

21

22

23

24

25

26

27

# *October/November*

28

29

30

31

1

2

3

# An early double dahlia

A hand-coloured stipple engraving by

<small>PIERRE-JOSEPH REDOUTÉ</small> from his *Choix des plus belles fleurs* (1827-33)

<small>ACCORDING TO CHARLOTTE DE LA TOUR</small>, a bouquet of dahlias signified '*Ma reconnaissance compasse vos soins*', but the only English writer to follow her in this definition was Robert Tyas in his *Language of Flowers* (1869): 'My gratitude exceeds your care'. Most English writers, including Tyas himself in earlier years, gave 'Instability' as the plant's meaning. *The Catholic Language of Flowers* (1861) redefined it as 'Ornament'.

A CULTIVAR OF

# Hydrangea macrophylla

A hand-coloured stipple engraving by

PIERRE-JOSEPH REDOUTÉ from his *Choix des plus belles fleurs* (1827-33)

CHARLOTTE DE LA TOUR USED THE HYDRANGEA to convey the message *'Vous êtes froide'*, but the early English books changed this to 'Boaster'. Some American writers, however, gave entries for both hydrangea and hortensia, possibly unaware that both names referred to the same plant, and gave 'You are cold' as the meaning for the latter.

4

5

6

7

8

9

10

# November

**11**

**12**

**13**

**14**

**15**

**16**

**17**

# Rosa centifolia

A hand-coloured stipple engraving by

PIERRE-JOSEPH REDOUTÉ from his *Les roses* (1817-24)

CHARLOTTE DE LA TOUR GAVE THE MEANING OF THIS ROSE as 'The Graces'. Most early language of flowers books, missing the classical allusion, modified this to 'Graces'. In some later books the meaning was changed to 'Pride' or 'Dignity of mind', and 'Grace' was given as the meaning of the Multiflora rose instead.

# Gladiolus undulatus

A hand-coloured stipple engraving by

Pierre-Joseph Redouté from his *Les liliacées* (1802-16)

THE GLADIOLUS WAS A SUBJECT of experimental plant breeding during the early nineteenth century but had to wait until late in the century before it became the popular flower it is today. Consequently it does not appear in the early books on the language of flowers. John Ingram, in his *Flora Symbolica* (1869), gives its meaning as 'Ready armed', drawing on its etymology (gladiolus = little sword).

18

19

20

21

22

23

24

# *November/December*

25

26

27

28

29

30

1

# Viola tricolor

A hand-coloured stipple engraving of heartsease pansies by

PIERRE-JOSEPH REDOUTÉ from his *Choix des plus belles fleurs* (1827-33)

HEARTSEASE PANSIES, as shown in Redouté's illustration, had the traditional meaning of 'Thought' (from the French *pensée*). When the modern pansy (cultivars of *Viola* × *wittrockiana*) was developed in about 1840, writers on the language of flowers kept 'Thought' as the meaning for both the old and the new plants. Some books offered slight variations such as 'You occupy my thoughts'.

# *Anemone coronaria*

A hand-coloured stipple engraving by

Pierre-Joseph Redouté from his *Choix des plus belles fleurs* (1827-33)

Charlotte de la Tour gave 'Abandon' as the meaning for the anemone, because in Greek mythology the nymph Anemone had been abandoned by her lover Zephyr. English writers translated this as 'Forsaken'. *The Catholic Language of Flowers* (1861) adapted this meaning slightly to 'Jesus forsaken'.

2

3

4

5

6

7

8

# December

9

10

11

12

13

14

15

# Digitalis purpurea

A hand-coloured stipple engraving of a common foxglove by

Ferdinand Bauer from John Lindley's *Digitalium Monographia* (1821)

In medieval times this plant was variously called 'Foxglove' and 'Our Lady's gloves'. After the Protestant Reformation, when associations with the Virgin Mary were discouraged in plant names, 'Foxglove' completely displaced its rival name. Not all language of flowers books included it, but those that did, including *The Catholic Language of Flowers* (1861), gave its meaning as 'Insincerity'.

# Acanthus mollis

A hand-coloured stipple engraving of acanthus by

Ferdinand Bauer from John Sibthorp's *Flora Graeca* (1806-40)

THE ACANTHUS, ACCORDING TO CLASSICAL TRADITION, was the model for the decoration of the Corinthian capital, and so it was appropriated as a symbol of the arts. That remained its meaning in the language of flowers until later books, perhaps through a misunderstanding, altered this to 'Artifice'.

16

17

18

19

20

21

22

# December

23

24

25

26

27

28

29

# An amaryllis or hippeastrum

A hand-coloured stipple engraving by

PIERRE-JOSEPH REDOUTÉ from his *Les liliacées* (1802-16)

WHEN IS AN AMARYLLIS NOT AN AMARYLLIS? Charlotte de la Tour reported that gardeners called it a proud plant, because it often refused to flower when they wanted, and she therefore made it a symbol of pride. But her 'amaryllis' included the Guernsey lily (*Nerine sarniensis*) as well as the plant now known as hippeastrum. In language of flowers books, 'Haughtiness' and 'Pride' remained the standard meanings of this group of plants, although, perversely, 'Timidity' was given as the meaning in an American work.

# *Myosotis scorpioides*

A hand-coloured stipple engraving of a forget-me-not by

Pierre-Joseph Redouté from his *Choix des plus belles fleurs* (1827-33)

IN THE SIXTEENTH CENTURY, the myosotis was apparently used as a lovers' charm; its French name, *'ne m'oubliez pas'*, was translated to form its common names in German and English. Accordingly 'Forget me not' became its standard meaning in the language of flowers. Some works gave 'True love' as an additional meaning.

30

31

1

2

3

4

5